THE MAHABHARATA
CHILDREN'S ILLUSTRATED CLASSICS

THE STORY of INDRAPRASTHA

Retold by CHARU AGARWAL DHANDIA
Art KAVITA SINGH KALE *Design* RACHITA RAKYAN

Published by
Rupa Publications India Pvt. Ltd 2020
7/16, Ansari Road, Daryaganj
New Delhi 110002

Sales centres:
Allahabad Bengaluru Chennai
Hyderabad Jaipur Kathmandu
Kolkata Mumbai

Edition copyright © Rupa Publications Pvt. Ltd 2020

All rights reserved.
No part of this publication may be reproduced, transmitted,
or stored in a retrieval system, in any form or by any means, electronic, mechanical, photocopying,
recording or otherwise,
without the prior permission of the publisher.

ISBN: 978-81-291-4974-9

First impression 2020

10 9 8 7 6 5 4 3 2 1

The moral right of the author has been asserted.

Printed at Nutech Print Services - India

This book is sold subject to the condition that it shall not, by way of trade or otherwise, be lent,
resold, hired out, or otherwise circulated, without the publisher's prior consent, in any form of
binding or cover other than that in which it is published.

Charu Agarwal Dhandia weaves together her two biggest passions—studying Indian classical literature and creative storytelling. She is an economist by training and works in the social development space.

Kavita Singh Kale's background as an artist and a designer enables her to draw a thin line between design following functionality and pure self-expression. This has helped her evolve as a transmedia artist. Her work includes art installations, children's books, comics, paintings and videos.

Rachita Rakyan combines over 15 years of expertise in graphic design and art direction with deep understanding of functionality and aesthetics across print, publishing, branding and digital media.

CONTENTS

KURU DYNASTY .... IV-V
KEY CHARACTERS .... VI-VII
DHRITHRASHTRA'S INVITATION 1
THE BARREN LAND 9
CITY OF INDRAPRASTHA 15
JARASANDHA 23
PANDAVAS IN MAGADHA 37
THE FIGHT 43

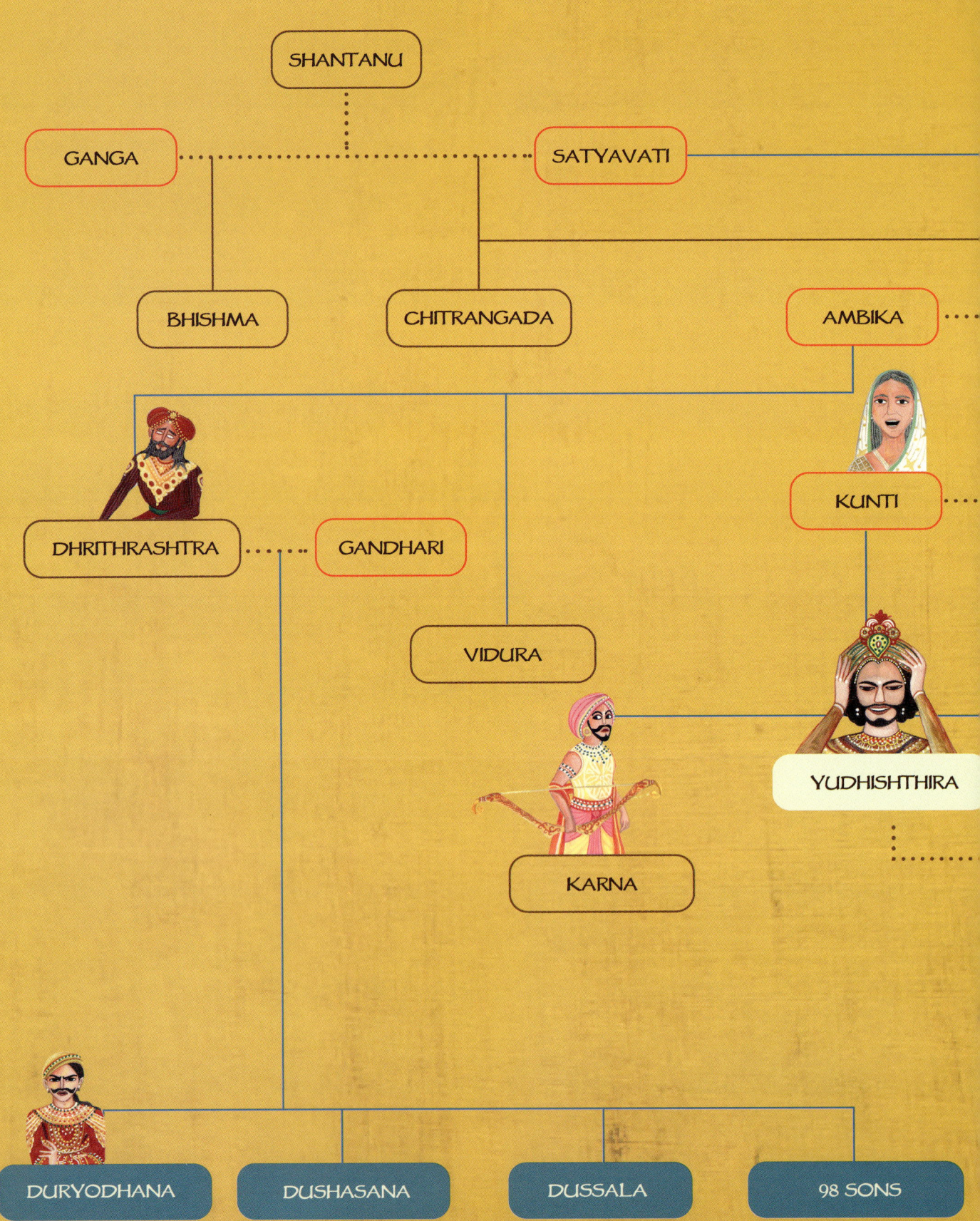

KURU DYNASTY

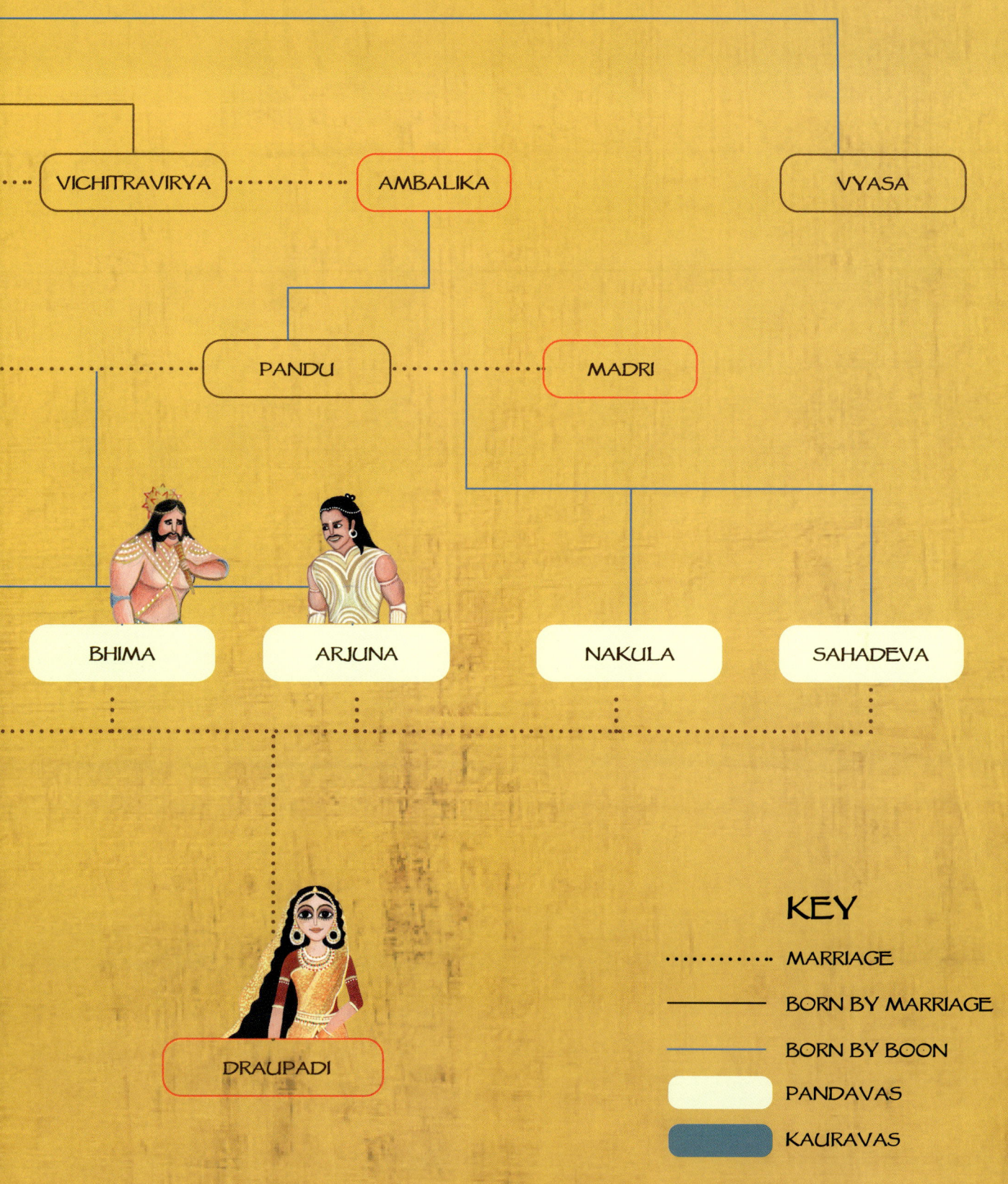

KEY CHARACTERS

KRISHNA

Krishna was the prince of Dwarka and cousin brother of the Pandavas and Kauravas. He was a great friend and advisor to Arjuna and loved the Pandavas dearly. He played a critical role in the creation of Indraprastha and later in the Kurukshetra War.

YUDHISHTHIRA

Yudhishthira was the eldest Pandava born to Kunti as a blessing from Lord Dharma. He ruled Indraprastha and later Hastinapur. Yudhishthira proved to be a great ruler and was known for his virtues of honesty, loyalty, justice, tolerance and brotherhood.

JARASANDHA

Jarasandha was the evil King of Magadh. He attacked kingdoms and kept the defeated kings locked up in his prison. He was born as two half bodies, joined by a demoness, Jara. Bhima later defeated him and set all captive kings free.

BHIMA

Bhima was the second of the Pandavas born to Kunti. He was immensely strong and protected his family from every danger. He married Hidimbi and later Draupadi.

DURYODHANA

Duryodhana was the eldest brother amongst the Kauravas and born to princess Gandhari as a blessing from sage Vyasa. He was very jealous of the Pandavas.

DHRITHRASHTRA

Dhrithrashtra was the blind king of Hastinapur. He was born to Queen Ambika by a boon given to her by the great sage Vyasa. Dhrithrashtra married Gandhari, daughter of the King of Gandhar. Together, they had a hundred sons called the Kauravas and a daughter called Dussala.

DHRITHRASHTRA'S INVITATION

Dhrithrashtra was the blind king of Hastinapur and the father of the Kaurava brothers. One morning, a messenger came to Dhrithrashtra and said, 'The Pandavas have won the competition in Panchala and have married princess Draupadi.'

Dhrithrashtra looked disappointed. His son Duryodhana had lost the competition to the Pandavas. Vidura was the minister of the court and uncle of the Pandavas and Kauravas. He turned to Dhrithrashtra and said, 'The Pandavas are the royal princes of the court. We must invite them to Hastinapur to celebrate their marriage.'

Dhrithrashtra nodded in agreement. The next day, a courtier reached Ekacharya to invite the Pandavas to Hastinapur. The Pandavas knew that Dhrithrashtra and Duryodhana were upset about losing the competition at Panchala.

They could not decide if they should accept the invitation. They discussed and discussed but did not know what to do. So, they decided to consult their cousin, the mighty Krishna.

Krishna heard the Pandavas and said, 'You must accept the invitation and go to Hastinapur. It is where your home and family are.'
The princes took Krishna's advice, and started preparing for Hastinapur.

THE BARREN LAND

The Pandavas left for Hastinapur with Draupadi and their mother Kunti. All this while, Dhrithrashtra and Duryodhana had been thinking of a plan to trick the Pandavas.
At a far end of Hastinapur, there was a useless piece of land which was barren and infested by demons. Duryodhana and Dhrithrashtra decided to gift this land to the Pandavas.

The Pandava princes reached Hastinapur and were welcomed with drums and garlands. They met Dhrithrashtra in his court and graciously accepted the land. They knew that the land was useless but accepted it with humility and respect for Dhrithrashtra.

For the next few days, the Pandavas wondered what to do with the land. It was dry, barren and nothing could grow on it. They thought for days but could not reach a solution. So they decided to consult Krishna again.

Krishna heard their problem and said, 'Look at the land as an opportunity to create something new for the people of Hastinapur. A city of dreams, wealth, prosperity and happiness!' The Pandavas smiled. They now knew what to do.

The Pandavas spent the next few days and nights in planning the new city. Masons, carpenters, painters and craftsmen from all over the country were called to build the dream city. The famous architect Mayasura, who was the greatest of all architects, was called to design the city.

Everyone watched curiously as the new kingdom started taking shape, brick by brick.

Soon, a wonderful city was created in the barren land. People from far and wide were amazed to see what the Pandavas had built! They named the gorgeous city Indraprastha, a city for the Gods.

Indraprastha was beautiful like a dream. There were marvellous structures with intricately carved pillars and polished floors shone like mirrors. Camels, elephants, chariots, jewels and riches were everywhere.

Soon, people from nearby kingdoms began moving into the city, and trade and businesses flourished.

Yudhishthira became the king of Indraprastha. He was a generous, kind and compassionate king. His people loved him dearly and respected him a lot.

JARASANDHA

One day, Yudhishthira was sitting alone in his chambers. Krishna came in to meet him. He wanted to tell Yudhishthira about the evil king Jarasandha, the ruler of Magadha.

Krishna said, 'Jarasandha is a very powerful but evil king. For years, Jarasandha has attacked and conquered many kingdoms, because he wants to be the most powerful king.'

'He has even kept the defeated kings locked up in his prison! We must go to Magadha, defeat Jarasandha and free the helpless kings.'

Yudhishthira told the other Pandavas about Jarasandha and they all agreed to go to Magadha, disguised as brahmins so that Jarasandha would not attack them. While they were travelling to Magadha, Krishna began to tell them the strange story of the birth of Jarasandha.

Long, long ago, there lived a king with his two wives. He was very unhappy because his wives could bear no children. There was no heir to the throne of Magadha! One day, the king met a sage in the forest. He told the sage about his problem and asked for help. The sage closed his eyes and prayed for some time.

Then he opened his eyes and gave a mango to the king. He said, "Take this mango and give it to your wife to eat. Soon you will be blessed with a child and your misery will be over."

The king jumped with joy. He took the mango and quickly returned to his palace. "But I have two wives and I love them both dearly. Which one of them should I give the mango to?" the king wondered. After thinking for a long time, he cut the mango from the middle and gave one half to each queen.

Each queen ate half of the magical mango and soon gave birth. Alas! Each queen gave birth to half a baby! Each baby had only one hand, one eye, one leg!

The king had made a big mistake by cutting the magical mango into two halves! The king and his wives were miserable.

Some days later, a demoness called Jara was passing by when she saw the two half-babies sleeping in a cot. She used her magic power to join the half-babies together, and lo and behold, There was one full baby in the cot! The king and his queens were thrilled to see the baby! They thanked Jara for her kindness and named the baby Jarasandha.

Jarasandha grew up to be very powerful and nobody could defeat him. But Krishna knew that Jarasandha could be defeated only if someone hit him at the centre, where the two halves were joined. That was Jarasandha's weakest point, but no one knew this secret.

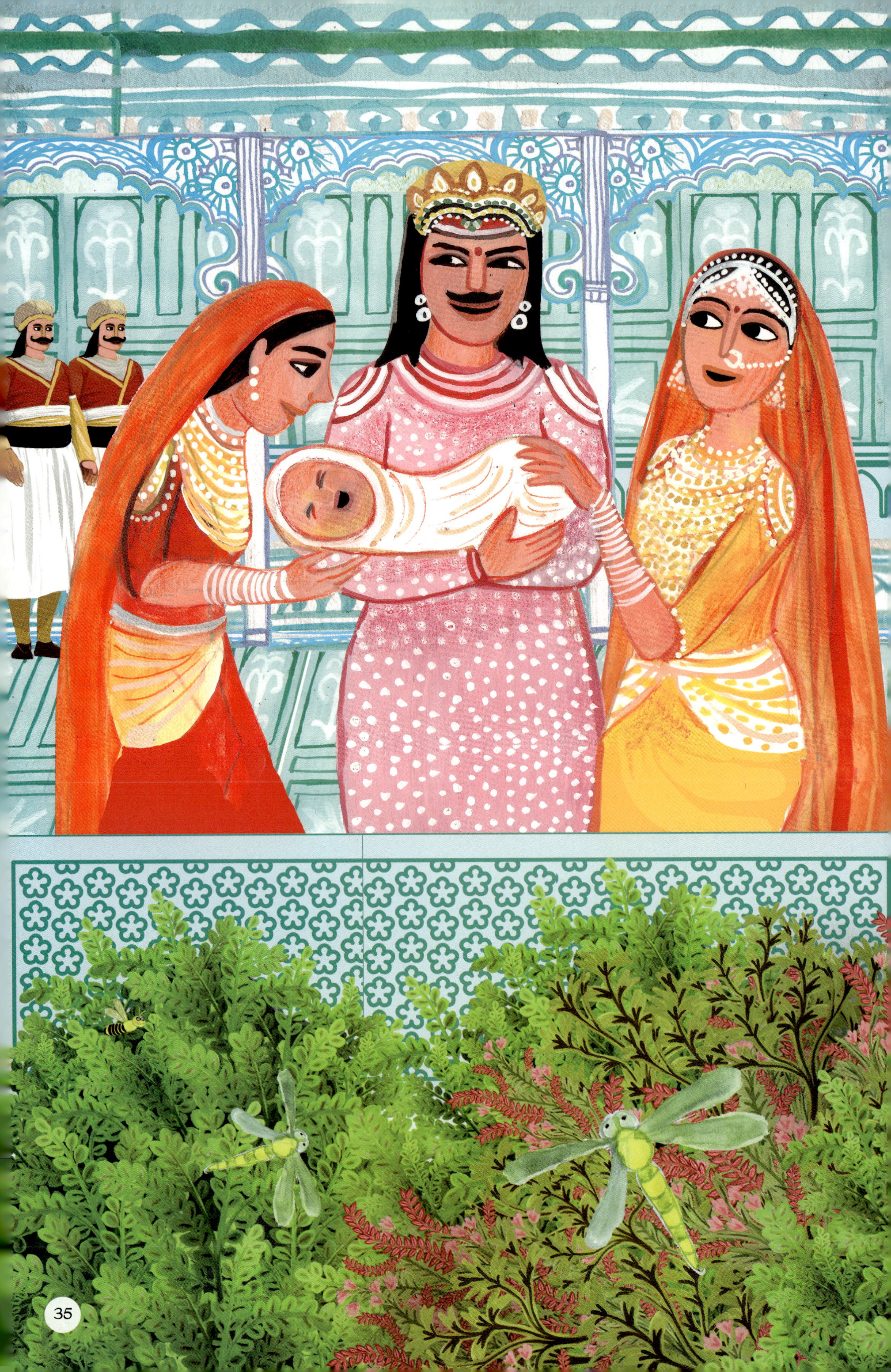

PANDAVAS IN MAGADHA

Soon the Pandavas reached Magadha. The palace had huge gates with guards at every corner. Since the Pandavas were disguised as brahmins, they entered easily. They roamed around the palace with other priests, keeping a close eye on Jarasandha.

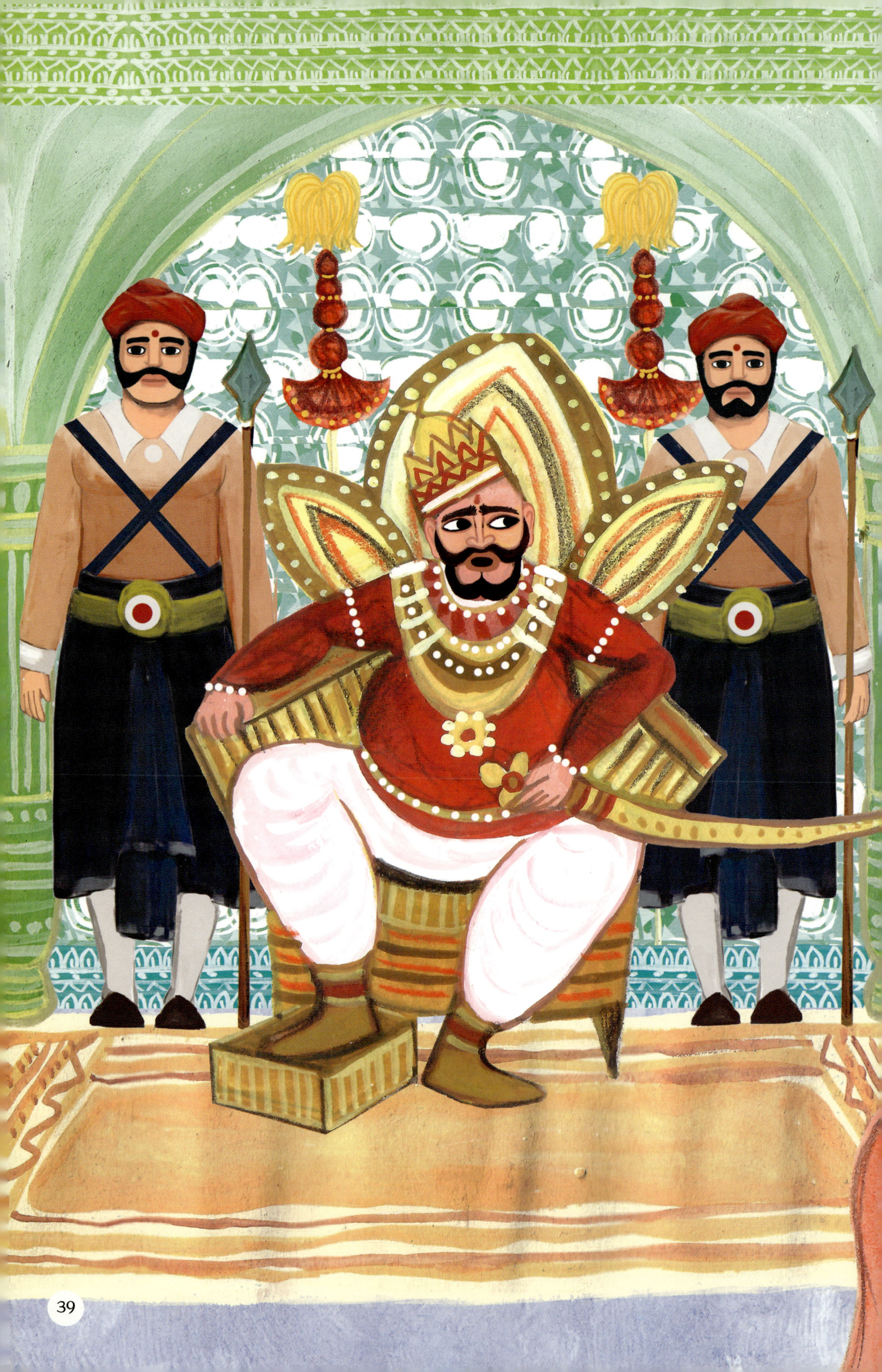

One evening, Jarasandha saw Krishna walking by and got suspicious. He asked his courtier to bring Krishna to his court.

Krishna entered with the Pandavas. Jarasandha looked at him and said, 'You are the mighty Krishna! Aren't you?'

'Yes, it is me! And these are the three brave Pandavas—Yudishthira, Arjuna and Bhima!' Krishna said, pointing at the princes.

Bhima said, 'Jarasandha, I am here to challenge you to a fight!' Everyone in the court was shocked!

Jarasandha laughed aloud. 'You think you can defeat me? I accept your challenge!'

'There are many princes who dared to challenge me, but are now held captive in my prison. I invite you to join them!' Jarasandha said proudly. His evil laughter filled the court. But the Pandavas were not scared.

'You are unaware of my brother Bhima's strength. We will see you at the fight, Jarasandha!' said Yudhishthira.

THE FIGHT

People gathered in hundreds to witness the fight between Jarasandha and Bhima. Great crowds settled in the arena and the fight began.

Bhima made several attempts to hit Jarasandha but the evil king bounced back with more force. Bhima did not know what to do. The fight went on for days. Every day, Jarasandha went back safely to his chambers, laughing at the Pandavas.

One day, Bhima suddenly remembered what Krishna had said. 'I must attack Jarasandha at the point where he was joined as a baby! That's the weakest place in his body!' So Bhima attacked Jarasandha in the middle of his body with all his force.

Immediately Jarasandha fell on the ground, unable to move. Bhima had defeated him!

The people of Magadha were relieved to be free from the evil King Jarasandha. The Pandavas freed all the kings and princes from the prison. People rejoiced everywhere and celebrations continued.

The Pandavas crowned Jarasandha's son as the new King of Magadha.

Yudhishthira and his brothers returned victorious to Indraprastha. With each passing day, Indraprastha became a happier place and the fame of the Pandavas spread far and wide.

TITLES IN THIS SERIES

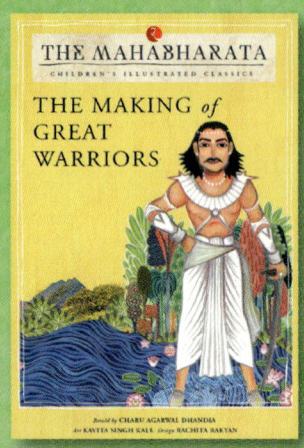
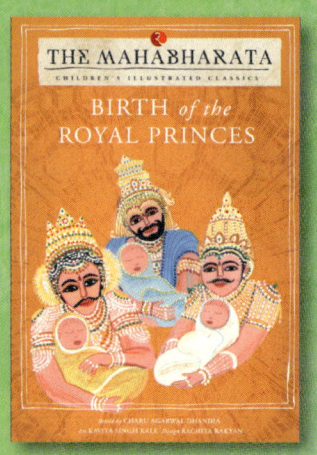
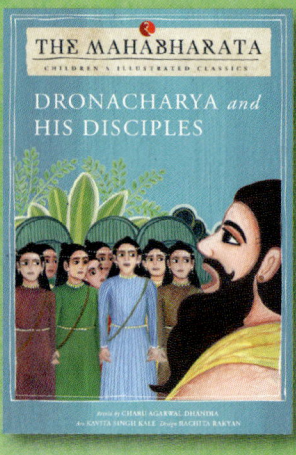
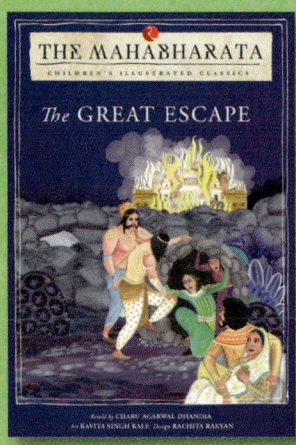
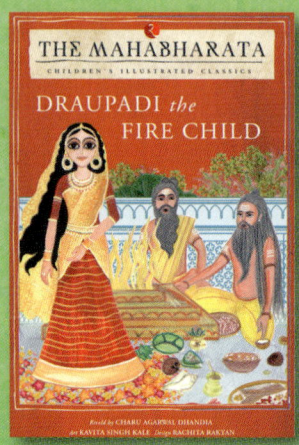
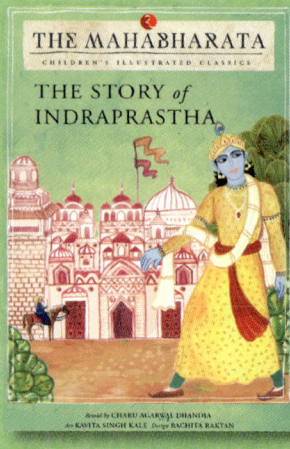
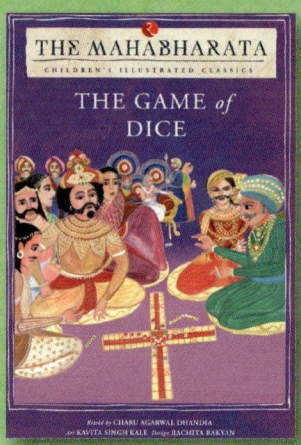
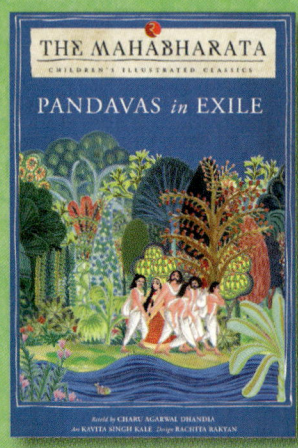
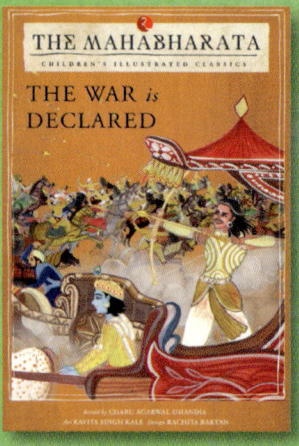